EGMONT
We bring stories to life

First published in Great Britain 2018
by Egmont UK Limited
The Yellow Building, 1 Nicholas Road, London W11 4AN

Illustrations by Ulises Farinas

© & ™ 2018 Lucasfilm Ltd.
ISBN 978 0 6035 7685 0
70433/001
Printed in Italy

To find more great *Star Wars* books, visit www.egmont.co.uk/starwars

Stay safe online. Any website addresses listed in this book are correct at the time of going to print. However, Egmont is not responsible for content hosted by third parties. Please be aware that online content can be subject to change and websites can contain content that is unsuitable for children. We advise that all children are supervised when using the internet.

Egmont takes its responsibility to the planet and its inhabitants very seriously.
We aim to use papers from well-managed forests run by responsible suppliers.

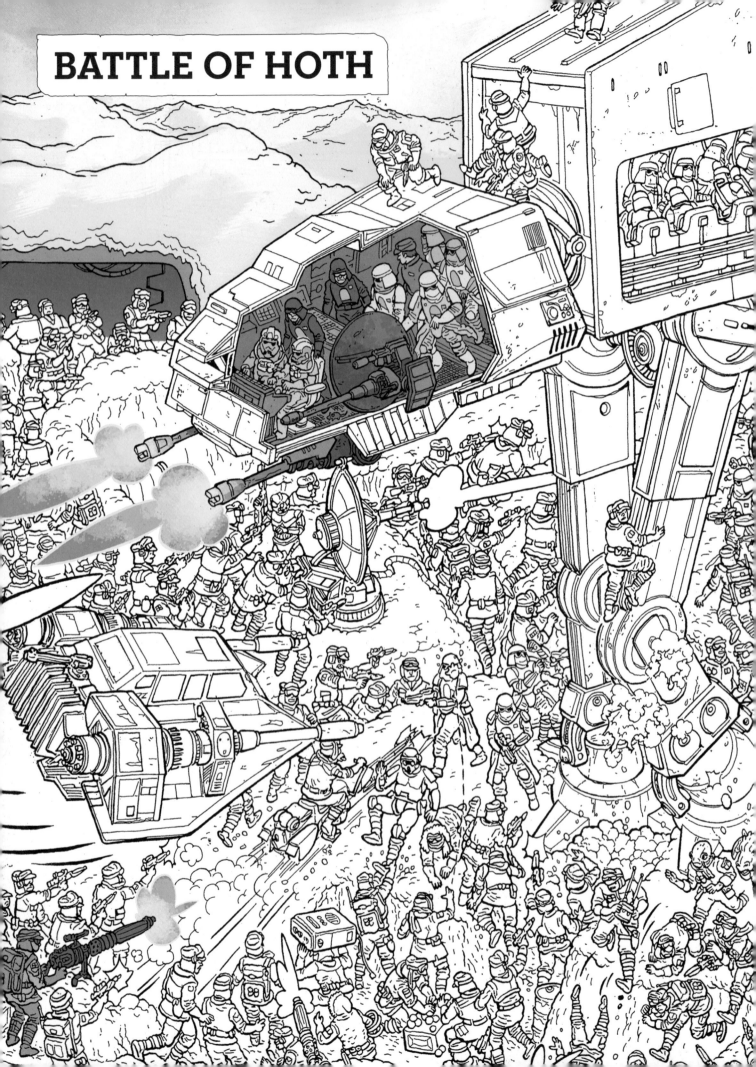

BATTLE OF HOTH

THE DEATH STAR

KASHYYYK

KAMINO

DROID FACTORY

HOME ONE

SCARIF